Bob Tells All

Sheila Hollins and Valerie Sinason
illustrated by Beth Webb

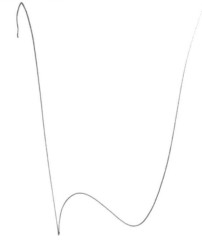

Beyond Words

London

5

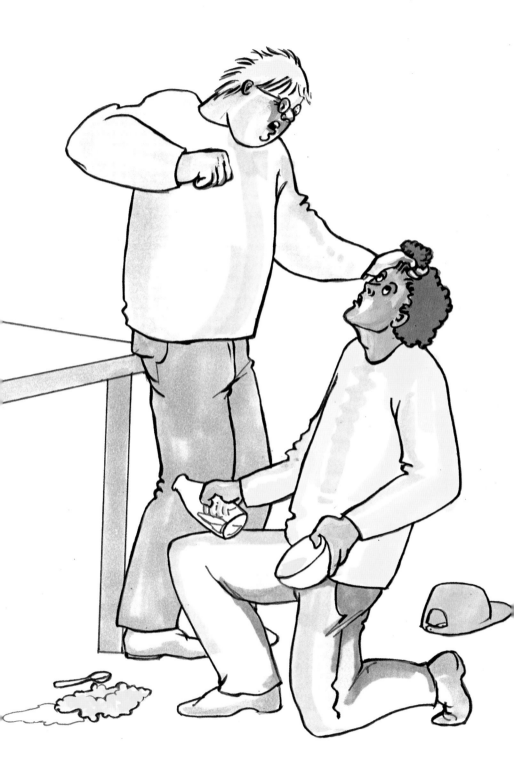

9

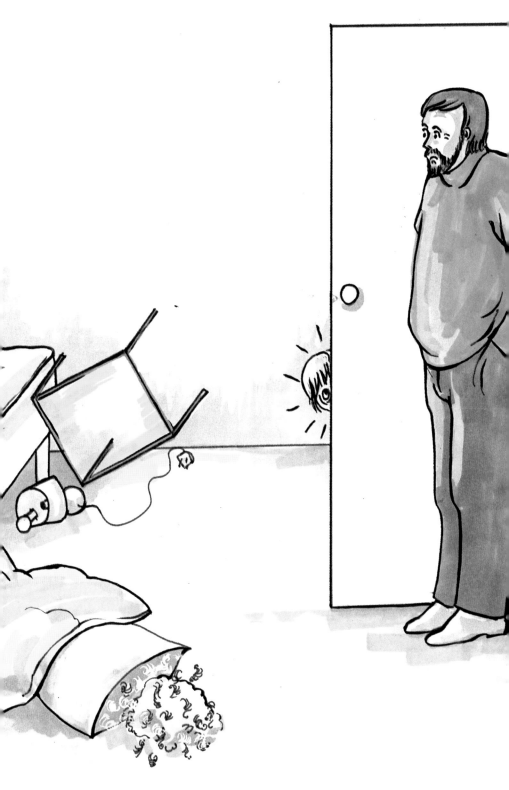

First published 1993 by St George's Mental Health Library.

This edition published 2015, by Books Beyond Words.

Text & illustrations © Books Beyond Words 2015.

ISBN 978-1-78458-057-5

British Library Cataloguing-in-Publication Data
A catalogue record for this book is available from the British Library.

Printed by DX Imaging, Watford.

Books Beyond Words is a Community Interest Company registered in England and Wales (7557861).

St George's Hospital Charity is a registered charity (no. 241527).

Contents   page

Storyline

The following words are provided for readers and supporters who want some ideas about one possible story. Most readers make their own story up from the pictures.

1. Bob moves to a group home.

2. Jon helps him unpack.

3. Bob likes his new friends.

4. In the night, Bob wakes everyone with his screaming.

5. Next morning, Bob is very upset.

6. "What's wrong?" asks Jon.

7. "Shut up or I'll give you one!" shouts Bob.

8. Bob smashes up his room.

9. Bob feels terrible. He doesn't know what to do.

10. Jon rings Steve, their social worker. Jon says, "We're all frightened of Bob!"

11. Steve comes straight away.

12. "Bob's upstairs!" says everyone.

13. Steve knocks on Bob's door.

14. Bob is scared.

15. Steve comes in and sees the mess.

16. He finds Bob hiding behind the door.

17. "Don't be afraid," says Steve. "I'm not going to hurt you."

18. "What's the matter?" asks Steve. "It's a secret," says Bob.

19. Bob clutches his trousers. Steve says, "Your trousers are private. Did you think I was going to touch them?"

20. "Yes!" shouts Bob.

21. "Has someone hurt your bottom?" asks Steve.

22. "He used to come in at night, and do things to my bum," says Bob. "It hurt and I didn't like it. He told me not to tell."

23. Steve listens carefully. "That's terrible," he says.

24. Bob tells Steve lots of things.

25. Jon knocks on the door. "Is Bob all right?" he asks.

26. "Bob has been hurt," says Steve. "He had a horrid time where he used to live."

27. "I'm sorry I frightened you," says Bob. "That's all right," says Jon.

28. Everyone helps Bob clear up.

29. At last everyone can relax. Steve says they have lots more talking to do.

Sexual abuse

When we first wrote this book, people did not want to think about sexual abuse. It is a very painful thing to think about. People still do not want to think about it but there is more understanding of how it hurts men and women. This book is about sexual abuse or rape of a man called Bob. Girls and women can read our book *Jenny Speaks Out*.

Bob is moving into a new house. A new house is like a new body. If your body has been hurt and you feel dirty then you do not like your body and you do not like a new house. You feel too sad and dirty.

Thinking about sexual abuse can hurt the body and mind. Lots of people are told to keep it a secret. That makes them feel even worse. Sometimes they show their hurt by staying away from people and not wanting to be friendly. Sometimes people show their hurt by getting too friendly with lots of people to try and drown their memories. They may get confused about their own sexual wishes and don't know if they are allowed to say no. Others don't know if they are allowed to say yes. Saying yes to the right person helps someone recover and to feel lovable again.

When somebody is raped by a member of their family or a family friend, it can be very hard to work out how to keep good memories about the person who has hurt them. People may feel that they have to break away completely. When someone is raped by a stranger who is cruel, it can make them feel they must be bad or it wouldn't have hurt so much. One of the hardest things for all victims of rape is feeling bad, dirty and unlovable. People often feel it must be their fault. That takes a long while to work through.

Because Bob has a good person looking out for him he is given a chance to communicate. When Bob faces his memory it makes him violent. Lots of people hurt themselves or things around them when their bodies and minds have been hurt by abuse.

Once Bob has told what happened to him, he can be helped but it is not easy. Sometimes telling about abuse and rape can bring the memories back even stronger. Sometimes people remember it in their heads like a film that will not stop, and it can wake them up at night too. Sometimes they cannot eat or they eat too much or they do not feel like washing. If there are good, understanding people around, then recovery can happen as it does for Bob. You can recover quickest from rape or sexual abuse if someone you trust believes you and helps you. Bob was lucky. Some people do not get listened to. Some men who hurt themselves are seen as problems because of what they do. No one asks why they do it.

With Bob, there is a quick road to recovery. However, when someone has not been listened to for years, or when someone is frightened that their abusers could still hurt them, they might need extra help. See our books *Supporting Victims* about reporting a crime, or *I Can Get Through It* about having counselling.

Safeguarding

Safeguarding is the term used to denote the measures used by local and national authorities, working in partnership with other services and the community, to protect children and adults at risk from harm and abuse. In the UK the law says that every organisation that works directly with children or with adults at risk must have a policy saying what should happen if someone reports abuse.

If someone reports abuse to you, this will mean that you need to take steps to make sure that the person is safe now and in the future. Depending on your job this might mean that you tell your line manager about the situation or you report it straight to the local authority social services department and/or to the police if there has been a crime.

Make sure that you know your organisation's safeguarding policy well. If you are not sure what to do, or you are a private individual, contact the local authority social services department for help.

Medical evidence

When someone is raped a crime has happened. This means that the police need to know. Anybody who rapes somebody needs help to stop, through treatment or prison or both. If they are not caught, they could hurt more people. Because rape is a crime, the police need evidence, and medical examination is the best way. Do not wash yourself or your clothes, or throw your clothes away, even though you may long to do so. The police doctor can get evidence about what happened from your body and your clothes, as well as from what you say. When abusers are found, and many are not, they usually say they did not do anything. This is why medical evidence is necessary.

Post-abuse treatment

Psychotherapy

Many children and adults who are struggling to make sense of a difficulty in their lives find a talking and listening treatment helpful – one of the many kinds of psychotherapy and counselling available in the NHS (National Health Service), as well as privately. It is very important that children and adults with learning disabilities and communication difficulties have the same access to treatment that other citizens do.

What is a talking treatment?

Even those of us with no speech are part of the world of language. We hear and understand something in words. Psychotherapy is an attempt, with words, to help to make sense of the problems we carry inside us and show to others through our behaviour, our feelings and our language – both verbal and non-verbal.

All such treatments, whether carried out by a nurse, psychologist, social worker or psychiatrist, who have received extra training in psychotherapy, or by trained psychotherapists who are approved by the BPC (British Psychoanalytic Council) or UKCP (UK Council for Psychotherapy), use words as the main way of communicating, even if the person does not speak or use signs. Sometimes a person may need extra help at the same time as therapy, for example medication or extra support at home.

With some adults with severe physical and/or learning disabilities, the therapist includes drawing materials and a range of objects that add to communication ability. For example, Sara Jones, aged 40, a woman with severe learning disabilities and physical disabilities, became depressed after a fall on her bathroom floor. She had no spoken speech and understood little language. However, because her therapist included a doll's house complete with furniture, she was able to demonstrate the act of falling over in the bathroom.

Who needs treatment?

Some families and individuals have long-standing deep problems but would never go for help, and some people go for help quickly. It is their own feelings that tell them whether they can untangle the worry by themselves. It is important to remember that while love and friendship both help, they cannot take away all emotional pain. Similarly, you cannot love someone out of an emotional problem or deep distress. You can support somebody and that makes a big difference. But there is an untangling process that may have to be done with someone else who is not involved.

How to get therapy

First, the person has to feel that there is a problem they need help with. Second, they have to be able to tell someone that they would like help in understanding a problem. Depending on somebody's age, the people to tell could include their parents, teachers, a supporter, a social worker, psychiatrist, a GP or someone from their place of worship if they are religious.

Once a letter is sent to the person's local psychotherapy service from their GP they will then wait for an appointment letter. Once this arrives the person will have from one to three meetings to explore their problem and see if they and the therapist think it would be a good idea to start psychotherapy. It may not be with the person who they first meet.

What happens in therapy?

For all talking therapies, people see the same person in the same room at the same time each week. Sometimes the person might not be able to go because they are not well or have to go somewhere else. Very occasionally the therapist may have to miss a session. Every few months there is another holiday – Christmas, Easter or Summer – and people miss therapy. However, because it is the same place and time almost every week, people build up a sense of safety and security in which it is possible to discuss their problems. In a talking therapy the therapist will only speak about subjects the person raises. It may be that the person does not want to talk about their particular problem and has other things on their mind. That is fine. Everything the person says or does is valued and will be thought about.

Usually, children and adults find it helpful to talk about their worries a little bit, once they feel safe with the therapist.

While our research shows that children and adults with learning disabilities, like everyone else, feel better as a result of therapy, therapy is not always easy. It can be painful remembering and talking about difficult things that have happened in your life. 'Getting through' sexual abuse will not be quick. People will need time and they may have ups and downs. However, there are important emotional rewards for people entering this treatment, including managing their life and feelings more easily. They may need help to go to their therapy sessions. Their supporters will need to understand that the person's sessions are private even if the person is upset before or after the sessions. Supporters will also need to remember that therapy cannot be the sole source of support.

Do people need therapy when they are sexually abused?

Sexual abuse is a betrayal of mind and body. Although it causes physical and emotional problems, not everyone needs treatment. Susan, aged 14, was abused by the driver who took her to her club. She told her mother the moment she got home and her mother believed her and called the police immediately. Although the case did not get to court, the fact that her mother had believed her right away had a big impact on Susan and she said she did not need to talk to anyone else about it.

Henry, aged 22, told his mother he had been abused by his grandfather. She was shocked and furious, and said he was a liar. Henry got sadder and sadder and did not even have the energy to eat. His GP got worried and arranged for therapy.

In other words, it is not just the fact that abuse has happened that makes someone need therapy, it is how it is dealt with by people close to them, and the individual's own personal resources.

Things people often say

Victim/survivors of abuse often believe things that their abuser has said to them, which add to the harm of the abuse itself.

Here are some of the false beliefs that many victim/survivors carry with them, and ways that you might be able to help them change their beliefs.

"It happened to me because I'm bad."

Answer: No, but this is what all victims are made to feel.

"It happened to me because I have a learning disability."

Answer: No, it happens to large numbers of girls, boys, men and women without learning disabilities too. It happens to people all over the world.

"It's my fault, because I like him/her and thought I could trust them."

Answer: Abusers are not just all bad. They can be very nice and kind when they are not in an abusing state of mind.

"It's my fault because I didn't say no or stop it happening, even though I knew I didn't want it to happen."

Answer: Sometimes the abuser will say that his victim wanted sex and enjoyed it. But it's hard to tell someone to stop, especially if you are frightened or confused and don't understand what is happening to you.

"I could never have sex again because I am dirty."

Answer: No. A medical examination will help you to know what has physically happened to your body, and talking to friends or a therapist will help you to look at what has happened to your mind. After you have washed there is no sign of what has happened. It is in your mind that you still feel dirty. Of course if the rape came when you were a virgin, it has changed you in a different way, because now you are not a virgin. If you got an infection from the person who raped you, this will need medical treatment before you can have sex with anyone else.

Useful resources

Services in the UK

Victim Support
Victim Support is the national charity for people affected by crime. It is an independent organisation, offering a free and confidential service, irrespective of whether or not a crime has been reported to the police. Staff and volunteers in local branches give emotional support, information and practical help to victims, witnesses, their relatives and friends. They also promote victims' and witnesses' rights in all aspects of criminal justice and social policy by lobbying the government for legislative change.
www.victimsupport.org.uk

Association of Child Abuse Lawyers (ACAL)
ACAL offers practical support for lawyers and other professionals working for adults and children who have been abused. A page on their website describes for survivors of abuse what they might expect to get from lawyers: www.childabuselawyers.com/survivors
www.childabuselawyers.com

Respond
Respond offers assessment and treatment to people with learning disabilities who are victims and/or perpetrators of sexual abuse, and advice, training and consultancy to carers and professionals.
www.respond.org.uk

Some areas have **Sexual Assault Referral Centres** (**SARC**s). They can offer you medical support and

42

collect evidence that can be used later. If appropriate, the police will ask you if you'd like to be referred, or you can go directly to the SARC yourself if you are not sure whether or not you want to report the incident. You can find your nearest rape and Sexual Assault Referral Centre service through the NHS Choices website:
www.nhs.uk/Service-Search/Rape-and-sexual-assault-referral-centres/LocationSearch/364

Rape Crisis
Rape Crisis is a national charity and the umbrella body for a network of independent member Rape Crisis organisations. Rape Crisis organisations provide a confidential helpline service for women and girls who have experienced any form of sexual violence at any time in their lives, as well as a range of other specialist support services. To find your nearest Rape Crisis Centre you can call the national Rape Crisis helpline or search on their website: www. rapecrisis.org.uk/centres.php
Freephone 0808 802 9999 (12.00pm–2.30pm, 7.00pm–9.30pm)

The Survivors Trust (TST)
TST is an umbrella organisation made up of 135 specialist rape, sexual violence and childhood sexual abuse support organisations throughout the UK and Ireland. Affiliated organisations provide a range of direct services to survivors including counselling, support, helplines and advocacy services. The TST website gives information about where victims of sexual abuse can find support. They also list Independent Sexual Violence Advisors (ISVAs) based across the country that can help victims understand

how the criminal justice process works and answer questions: www.thesurvivorstrust.org/isva/

Written materials and online resources

Change
On this website you can buy booklets about abuse, to help people with learning disabilities look after themselves: Sexual Abuse, Say No to Child Abuse, and What is Safeguarding?
www.changepeople.org

Abuse is Bad. By Speak Up Self-Advocacy. A DVD, produced by **Speak Up Self-Advocacy**, to give people with learning disabilities information about abuse. Copies can be ordered from the Friendly Resource catalogue.
www.friendlyresource.org.uk/

Abuse in Care? A practical guide to protecting people with learning disabilities from abuse in residential services. This guide offers information for health and social care staff:
www2.hull.ac.uk/fass/pdf/Abuse%20in%20Care%202. pdf

Protecting adults at risk: London multi-agency policy and procedures to safeguard adults from abuse. A guide to how organisations should work together to prevent abuse and harm.
Safeguarding adults at risk of harm: A legal guide for practitioners. An in-depth guide to the legal framework for safeguarding adults.
These guides are available from the **Social Care Institute for Excellence**:
www.scie.org.uk/adults/safeguarding/policies

Surviving Sexual Abuse – what you can do if you think you have been sexually abused. An easy read guide produced by **Enable Scotland** that explains what you can do if you have been sexually abused, and where you can get help and support. A guide for family carers and support staff, Unlocking sexual abuse and learning disabilities, is also available. Both guides are free to download: www.enable.org.uk/families/Over 18/Pages/Dealing-with-abuse.aspx

NSPCC and **Mencap** have produced two easy read guides to help keep children safe from sexual abuse. Part of the Underwear Rule campaign, one guide is for parents or carers with a learning disability, and the other guide is for children with a learning disability. NPSCC and the National Autistic Society have also produced a guide for parents of children with autism. All the guides can be downloaded for free from the NSPCC website: www.nspcc.org.uk/preventing-abuse/keeping-children-safe/underwear-rule/

Principles of safeguarding and protection for learning disability workers, by Simon Bickerton. Part of the **BILD** good support series, this book introduces the important topic of safeguarding people with a learning disability from abuse. It identifies different types of abuse and the possible signs and symptoms that might indicate that abuse has occurred. It explores why people with a learning disability might be more vulnerable to abuse and what the reader must do if abuse is suspected or alleged. Available through the BILD website: www.bild.org.uk/our-services/books/

Related titles in the Books Beyond Words series

Jenny Speaks Out (2015, 3rd edition) by Sheila Hollins and Valerie Sinason, illustrated by Beth Webb. Jenny feels unsettled when she moves into a new home in the community. Her carer and friends sensitively help Jenny to unravel her painful past as a victim of sexual abuse, and begin a slow but positive healing process.

I Can Get Through It (2009, 2nd edition) by Sheila Hollins, Christiana Horrocks and Valerie Sinason, illustrated by Lisa Kopper. This book tells the story of a woman whose life is suddenly disturbed by an act of abuse. It shows how with the help of friends and counselling, the memory of the abuse slowly fades.

When Dad Hurts Mum (2014) by Sheila Hollins, Patricia Scotland and Noëlle Blackman, illustrated by Anne-Marie Perks. After her dad is violent towards her mum, Katie is sad and distracted at college. Her teacher supports the family to get the help of an Independent Domestic Violence Advocate and the police. Katie and her mum are kept safe. Katie's dad is court-ordered to join a group to stop his abusive behaviour.

Finding a Safe Place from Abuse (2015) by Sheila Hollins, Patricia Scotland and Noëlle Blackman, illustrated by Anne-Marie Perks. Katie meets David and falls in love. She moves in with him, but the relationship turns difficult and dangerous when David begins to steal her money and hurt her. Katie quickly gets help through her GP. After a stay in a refuge, Katie begins a new life with a new sense of confidence.

Sonia's Feeling Sad (2011) by Shelia Hollins and Roger Banks, illustrated by Lisa Kopper. Sonia is feeling so sad that she shuts herself off from her family and friends. She agrees to see a counsellor and gradually begins to feel better.

Ron's Feeling Blue (2011, 2nd edition) by Sheila Hollins, Roger Banks and Jenny Curran, illustrated by Beth Webb. Ron is depressed and has no interest in doing things. With the help of his GP and family he begins to feel better.

Mugged (2002, 2nd edition) by Sheila Hollins, Christiana Horrocks and Valerie Sinason, illustrated by Lisa Kopper. This book tells the story of Charlie who is attacked in the street. The pictures show how Charlie is helped by speedy police action, Victim Support and back-up from friends, family and supporters.

Supporting Victims (2007) by Sheila Hollins, Kathryn Stone and Valerie Sinason, illustrated by Catherine Brighton. Polly is the victim of an assault. The book shows her experience as a witness at court, outlining the support and special measures that help her to give evidence.

Authors and artist

Sheila Hollins is Emeritus Professor of Psychiatry of Disability at St George's, University of London, and sits in the House of Lords. She is a past President of the Royal College of Psychiatrists and of the BMA, and chairs the BMA's Board of Science. She is founding editor, author and Executive Chair of Books Beyond Words, and a family carer for her son who has a learning disability.

Valerie Sinason is an Adult Psychoanalyst and Child Psychotherapist, and specialises in disability, trauma and abuse. She is Director of the Clinic of Dissociative Studies and President of the Institute of Psychotherapy and Disability. She is a poet and writer, and had a grandmother with a learning disability.

Beth Webb is the artist who helped to develop the very first Beyond Words books, linking emotionally-keyed colours with clear body language to enhance the simple illustrations. She is also a children's author and a professional storyteller.

Dedication

To all those people with learning disabilities who have shared their experience of abuse with us.

Beyond Words: publications and training

Books Beyond Words will help family carers, support workers and professionals working with people who find pictures easier than words for understanding their world. A list of all Beyond Words publications, including Books Beyond Words titles, and where to buy them, can be found on our website:

www.booksbeyondwords.co.uk

Workshops about using Books Beyond Words are provided regularly in London, or can be arranged in other localities on request. Self-advocates are welcome. For information about forthcoming workshops see our website or contact us:

email: training@booksbeyondwords.co.uk
tel: 020 8725 5512

Video clips showing our books being read are also on our website and YouTube channel: www.youtube.com/user/booksbeyondwords and on our DVD, *How to Use Books Beyond Words*.

How to read this book

There is no right or wrong way to read this book. Remember it is not necessary to be able to read the words.

1. Some people are not used to reading books. Start at the beginning and read the story in each picture. Encourage the reader to hold the book themselves and to turn the pages at their own pace.

2. Whether you are reading the book with one person or with a group, encourage them to tell the story in their own words. You will discover what each person thinks is happening, what they already know, and how they feel. You may think something different is happening in the pictures yourself, but that doesn't matter. Wait to see if their ideas change as the story develops. Don't challenge the reader(s) or suggest their ideas are wrong.

3. Some pictures may be more difficult to understand. It can help to prompt the people you are supporting, for example:

- Who do you think that is?
- What is happening?
- What is he or she doing now?
- How is he or she feeling?
- Do you feel like that? Has it happened to you/ your friend/ your family?

4. You don't have to read the whole book in one sitting. Allow people enough time to follow the pictures at their own pace.

5. Some people will not be able to follow the story, but they may be able to understand some of the pictures. Stay a little longer with the pictures that interest them.